Read, Search & Find®

DINOSAURS

Kidsbooks®

Illustrations Copyright © 2012, Orpheus Books Ltd
2 Church Green Witney, Oxon OX28 4AW

Illustrated by Peter Dennis (Linda Rogers Associates)
Written by Molly J. Markey, PhD, Science Writer and Paleontology Specialist

Text and Design Copyright © 2012, 2014 Kidsbooks, LLC.
Read, Search & Find is a registered trademark of Kidsbooks, LLC.
3535 West Peterson Avenue
Chicago, IL 60659

Printed in China
081402026JZ

Visit us at **www.kidsbooks.com**

Contents

Introduction 5

A Time Line of Life on Earth 6–7

Cambrian Seas 8–9

Devonian–Permian 10–11

Triassic–Cretaceous 12–13

Triassic 14–15

Jurassic 16–17

Cretaceous 18–19

Pterosaurs 20–21

Marine Reptiles 22–23

Fieldwork 24–25

Find Out More 26–31

Introduction

Millions of years ago, strange and interesting creatures roamed the earth: in the water, on land, and in the sky.

DINOSAURS will introduce you to many of the most fascinating creatures from those long-gone days. You'll learn about the time when all life was in the ocean, the movement of animals onto land, the rise of the dinosaurs, and more! Through fun Search & Find® activities, you'll identify different dinosaurs and other ancient animals and discover strange facts you could never imagine.

Dig into the **Find Out More** section in the back of this book to discover even more cool details about the different kinds of animals that lived long before humans.

So put on your paleontologist hat and get ready to **Read, Search & Find®** all about the age of the dinosaurs!

A Time Line of Life on Earth

PALEOZOIC ERA

Cambrian Period 542–488 mya
Ordovician Period 488–443 mya
Silurian Period 443–415 mya
Devonian Period 415–360 mya
Carboniferous Period 360–299 mya
Permian Period 299–251 mya

The Paleozoic Era was when living things became widespread, abundant, and important parts of Earth's landscape.

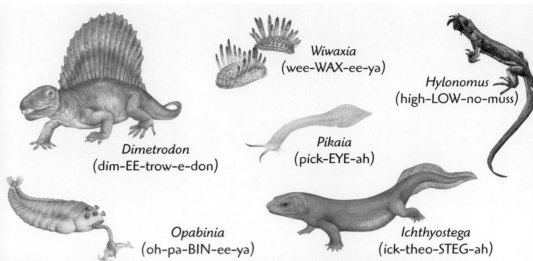

Wiwaxia
(wee-WAX-ee-ya)

Hylonomus
(high-LOW-no-muss)

Dimetrodon
(dim-EE-trow-e-don)

Pikaia
(pick-EYE-ah)

Opabinia
(oh-pa-BIN-ee-ya)

Ichthyostega
(ick-theo-STEG-ah)

MESOZOIC ERA

Triassic Period 251–200 mya
Jurassic Period 200–146 mya
Cretaceous Period 146–65 mya

The Mesozoic Era was the Age of Dinosaurs. Many other groups of organisms arose and thrived during the Mesozoic Era, too, such as turtles, pterosaurs, frogs, ichthyosaurs, birds, mammals, flowering plants, and modern ray-finned fishes. But some of these groups, including dinosaurs, pterosaurs, and ichthyosaurs, went extinct at the end of the Mesozoic.

Parasaurolophus
(par-a-sore-oh-LOW-fuss)

Tyrannosaurus rex
(tie-ran-oh-SORE-us recks)

Eudimorphodon
(you-di-MORE-foe-don)

Triceratops
(try-SAIR-uh-tops)

Ichthyosaurus
(ick-theo-SORE-us)

Allosaurus
(al-oh-SORE-us)

CENOZOIC ERA

Paleogene Period 65–23 mya
Neogene Period 23–2.6 mya
Quaternary Period 2.6 mya–present

The Cenozoic Era is the Age of Mammals.

mya* stands for *million years ago

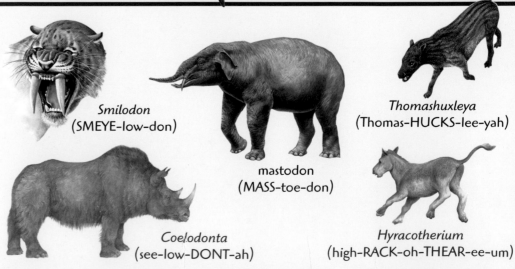

Smilodon
(SMEYE-low-don)

Thomashuxleya
(Thomas-HUCKS-lee-yah)

mastodon
(MASS-toe-don)

Coelodonta
(see-low-DONT-ah)

Hyracotherium
(high-RACK-oh-THEAR-ee-um)

6

thelodont
(thee-low-DONT)

Eryops
(EAR-yops)

trilobite
(TRY-low-bite)

Eusthenopteron
(use-thin-OP-terr-ahn)

Moschops
(MOW-shops)

Dunkleosteus
(dunk-ul-AH-stee-us)

Anomalocaris
(ann-o-mallow-CARE-is)

Thrinaxodon
(thrin-AXE-oh-dawn)

Morganucodon
(mor-gan-OO-co-dawn)

Microraptor
(MI-cro-rap-tor)

Archaeopteryx
(ark-ay-OP-terr-ix)

Eoraptor
(ee-yo-RAP-tor)

Plateosaurus
(plate-ee-oh-SORE-us)

Ankylosaurus
(ahnk-eye-low-SORE-us)

Stegosaurus
(steg-o-SORE-us)

Caudipteryx
(cod-IP-terr-ix)

Lystrosaurus
(list-trow-SORE-us)

Brachiosaurus
(brack-ee-o-SORE-us)

mammoth
(MAMM-uth)

Aepycamelus
(AY-pee-CAM-ell-us)

Indricotherium
(in-drick-oh-THEER-ee-um)

Macrauchenia
(mack-raw-SHEN-ee-ya)

Homo sapiens

Andrewsarchus
(andrew SARC-us)

Cambrian Seas

542–488 mya

During the Cambrian Period, members of major animal groups first appeared in Earth's oceans. If you could go snorkeling in the Cambrian seas, you probably wouldn't recognize most of the creatures. Many of them were evolutionary experiments that don't have living relatives today! Even animals that are related to living groups looked very different from their modern-day descendants.

Search & find the following creatures.

Trilobite
(TRY-low-bite)
This distant relative of today's spiders, horseshoe crabs, and lobsters lived on our planet for over 300 million years.

Marella
(mar-ELLA)
Very well-preserved fossils of *Marella* show that this arthropod had an iridescent (shiny) exoskeleton.

Pikaia
(pick-EYE-ah)
This is one of your ancestors! It had a structure like a backbone called a notochord. Human embryos have a notochord, but it is soon replaced by bone.

Wiwaxia
(wee-WAX-ee-ya)
Wiwaxia had no eyes or tentacles, and probably had to rely on its sense of smell or taste to find the microorganisms it ate.

Anomalocaris
(ann-o-mallow-CARE-is)
At 2 feet in length, *Anomalocaris* was the largest predator that stalked the Cambrian seas. It used its spiked tentacles to catch trilobites and early vertebrates!

Opabinia
(oh-pa-BIN-ee-ya)
This unique creature had five eyes on stalks and a nozzle like a vacuum cleaner for a mouth!

Hallucigenia
(hal-oo-suh-JEN-ee-ya)
With its tentacle-like limbs and sharp spines on its back, *Hallucigenia* looks very unlike the ocean-dwelling worms that are its closest living relatives.

Find Out More
on page 26

8

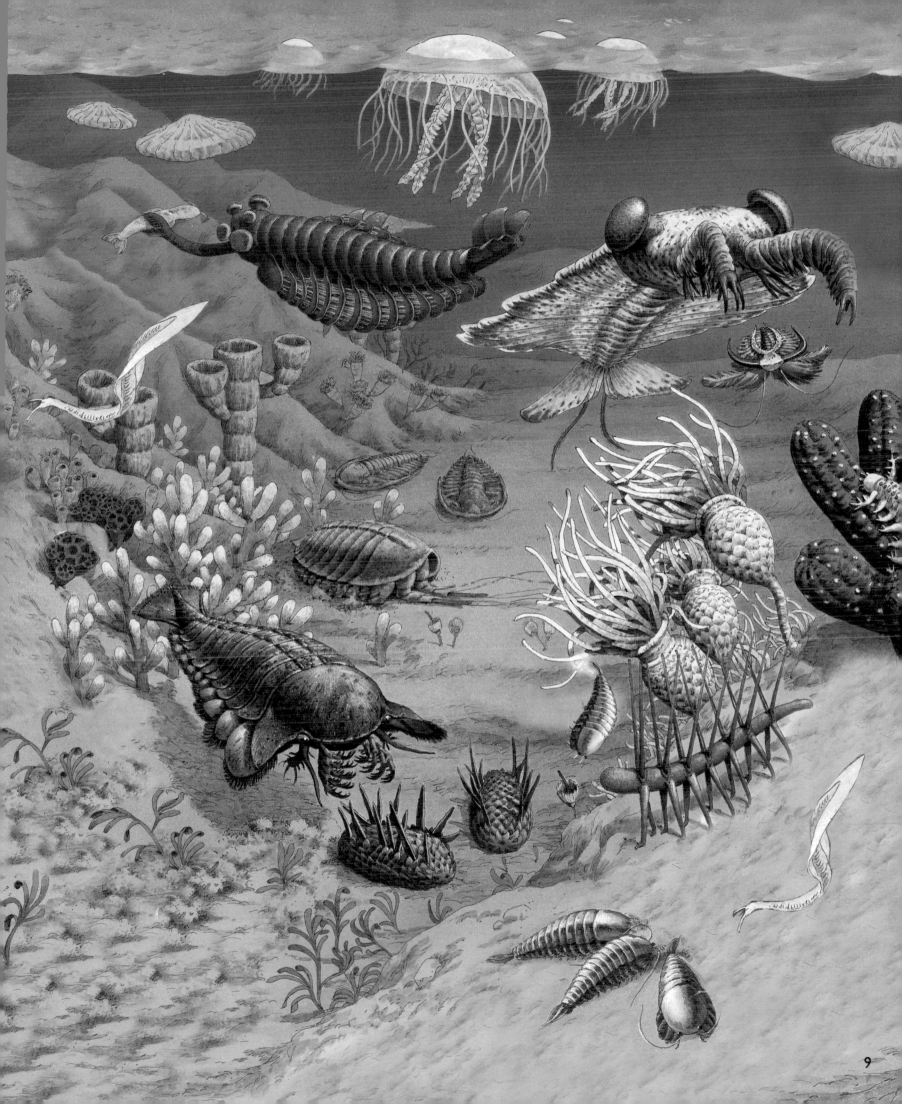

Devonian–Permian

415–251 mya

Paleontologists trace the beginning of our own story—the story of four-limbed land animals—to the Devonian Period. During the same time, land plants spread across the earth, and the first trees and forests also emerged. By the Carboniferous Period, the first reptiles appeared. During the Permian Period, primitive amphibians with sturdy limbs and reinforced backbones thrived.

Search & find the following animals.

Find Out More on page 27

Dimetrodon
(dim-EE-trow-e-don)
Dimetrodon is more closely related to you than it is to any reptile alive today! The large sail on its back may have helped it warm up and cool off.

Moschops
(MOW-shops)
Some mammal-like reptiles, like *Moschops*, were trying out a new way of eating during the Permian—they began eating plants.

Coelurosauravus
(SEE-loor-oh-SORE-oh-vus)
This reptile could not truly fly; it glided using "wings" made from skin stretched over long, thin bones that grew from the tips of its ribs.

Ichthyostega
(ick-theo-STEG-ah)

One of the earliest four-legged animals was *Ichthyostega*, an amphibious creature that had seven toes on each foot!

Hylonomus
(high-LOW-no-muss)

This early reptile laid tough-shelled eggs, allowing it to reproduce on dry land. (Amphibians lay their eggs in water so they won't dry out!)

Eusthenopteron
(use-thin-OP-terr-ahn)

This early fish had lungs like you and, within its fleshy "lobe fins," the bones that gave rise to your wrist, hand, foot, and ankle bones.

Eryops
(EAR-yops)

One of the largest amphibians to ever live on Earth, *Eryops* had a crocodile-like skull filled with large pointy teeth.

11

Triassic–Cretaceous

251–65 mya

Dinosaurs and many other groups of animals—including turtles, pterosaurs, mammals, and frogs—evolved in the Triassic Period. But dinosaurs were the most common, diverse, and largest animals on Earth for about 165 million years, from the Triassic to the Cretaceous Period. Dinosaurs lived on all continents on the planet (including Antarctica), but no dinosaurs lived in the water or flew.

Search & find the following items.

Styracosaurus

(sty-rack-oh-SORE-us)
With seven massive horns on its 6-foot-long skull, *Styracosaurus* was equipped to defend itself from predators like *Tyrannosaurus rex* and *Spinosaurus*.

Morganucodon

(mor-gan-OO-co-dawn)
One of the first true mammals, this creature was about the size of a shrew, was covered with fur, and ate insects. It also probably laid eggs.

Coelophysis
(see-low-FI-sus)
A fast-moving, lightly built predator, *Coelophysis* might have hunted in packs.

Proterosuchus
(pro-tayr-oh-SOO-cuss)
Crocodylians like this one gave rise to many different groups, including dinosaurs, pterosaurs, and the ancestors of today's crocodiles and alligators.

Lystrosaurus
(list-trow-SORE-us)
This herbivorous mammal-like reptile had two large tusks, but no other teeth. It was about the size of a pig.

Angiosperm
(ANJ-ee-oh-spurm)
These flowering plants surround their seeds with fruit. They became common in the early Cretaceous Period.

Archaeopteryx
(ark-ay-OP-terr-ix)
One of the earliest birds, this animal looked a lot like modern birds, but its beak held teeth and it had a long, bony tail.

Find Out More on page 27

Triassic

251–200 mya

The Triassic Period introduced many new creatures to the world, including the first dinosaurs and mammals. Plant life changed, too, with conifers and cycads making up most forests. Many groups of reptiles lived on Earth during the Triassic, and one of these groups gave rise to dinosaurs.

Search & find the following items.

Saltopus
(salt-OH-pus)

Saltopus, a rabbit-size, two-legged carnivore, was probably not a dinosaur. Unlike dinosaurs, it had five fingers on its hands.

Ornithosuchus
(or-nith-oh-SOO-kus)

This crocodylian was part of the group that evolved into modern crocodiles in the Cretaceous Period.

Horsetail
Horsetails were important ground cover plants in the Triassic—grass didn't evolve until millions of years later, during the Cretaceous Period.

Mussasaurus
(muss-uh-SORE-us)
The smallest known dinosaur fossil is a 3-centimeter-long infant *Mussasaurus* ("mouse lizard") skull found in Argentina.

Plateosaurus
(plate-ee-oh-SORE-us)
Although *Plateosaurus* probably walked on all fours most of the time, it might have been able to stand on two legs while feeding from tall trees.

Herrerasaurus
(hair-air-ah-SORE-us)
Herrerasaurus was first thought to be a dinosaur, but based on the shapes of its hip bones, it might just be a close relative.

Find Out More on page 28

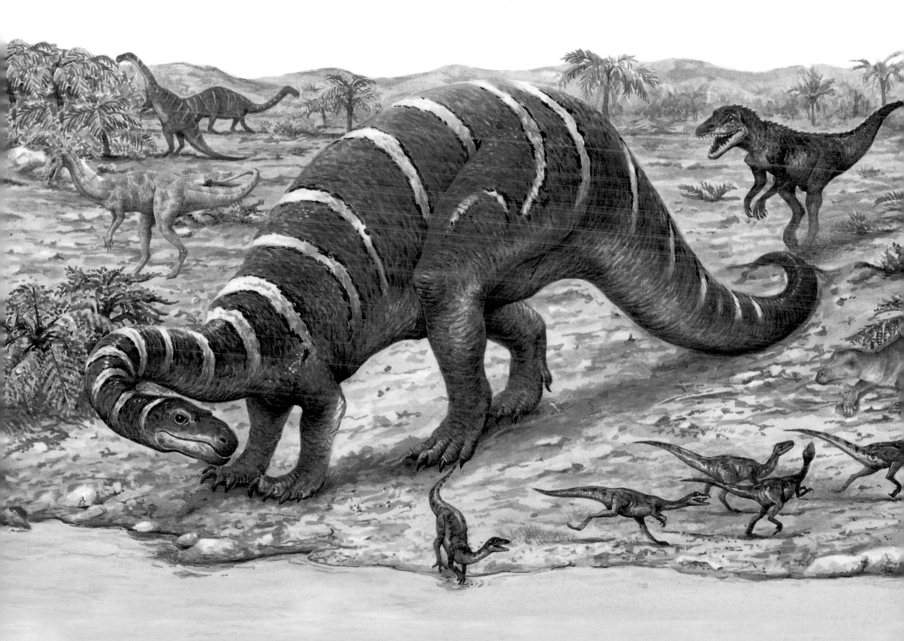

Jurassic

200–146 mya

During the Jurassic Period, dinosaurs became very large.
Long-necked sauropods became common, and plated stegosaurs also evolved. Although the first birds, including *Archaeopteryx*, evolved from small carnivorous dinosaurs in the Jurassic, the skies were dominated by pterosaurs. Mammals continued to evolve, but they were fairly unimportant parts of the Jurassic ecosystem.

Search & find the following items.

Allosaurus
(al-oh-SORE-us)
This 30-foot-long carnivorous dinosaur would wait for its prey to get very close before attacking.

Ceratosaurus
(serr-at-oh-SORE-us)
This meat-eating dinosaur had rows of small bony plates running down its back and ridges of bone in front of its eyes.

Stegosaurus
(steg-o-SORE-us)
The bony plates on *Stegosaurus*'s back might have protected it from predatory dinosaurs, or they may have helped it to warm up or cool down.

Sauropods
(SORE-oh-pods)
The plant-eating, long-necked, long-tailed sauropods are the largest land-dwelling animals to ever live on our planet.

Tree Fern
Tree ferns like this were common in the Jurassic Period, as were conifers (evergreens). Broadleaf trees weren't widespread until the Cretaceous Period.

Shunosaurus
(shoon-oh-SORE-us)
This unusual sauropod had armor-like scales on its back and a spiked club made of bone at the end of its tail.

Find Out More
on page 28

Cretaceous
146 to 65 mya

The first flowering plants appeared during the Cretaceous Period, along with bees, ants, butterflies, grasshoppers, and some other modern insects. This was also the end of the Age of Dinosaurs—by the end of the Cretaceous, all dinosaurs, the pterosaurs, the great marine reptiles, and many other species were extinct. In fact, half of all plants and animals went extinct at the end of the Cretaceous.

Search & find the following dinosaurs.

Tyrannosaurus rex
(tie-ran-oh-SORE-us recks)
At fully 35 to 40 feet long, *T. rex* was one of the largest predators ever to live on land.

Triceratops
(try-SAIR-uh-tops)
This dinosaur had a nearly solid wall of up to forty teeth on each side of its upper and lower jaws.

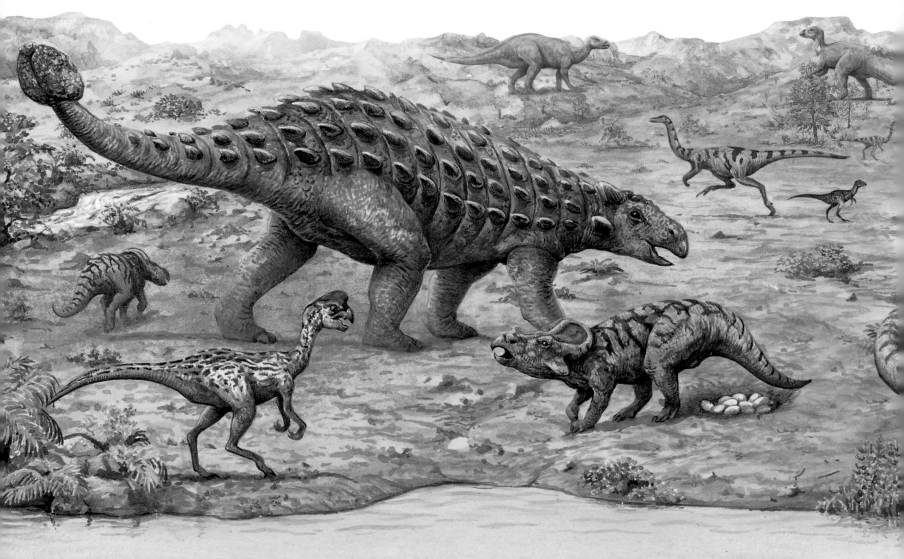

Corythosaurus
(core-ith-oh-SORE-us)
This duck-billed dinosaur had a bizarre bony crest on its head, which might have helped it produce loud bellows or calls.

Protoceratops
(pro-to-SAIR-uh-tops)
Protoceratops is the only dinosaur that has been preserved along with its footprints, so we know exactly what kind of tracks it made!

Oviraptor
(oh-vee-RAP-tor)
Fossils of these small carnivorous dinosaurs have been found on top of their nests; they died trying to protect their eggs from a sandstorm.

Baryonyx
(barry-ON-nix)
With small pointed teeth, narrow jaws, and hooked claws, *Baryonyx* was well adapted to catch fish for its food, a rare example of a piscivorous (fish-eating) dinosaur.

Iguanodon
(ig-WAHN-oh-don)
This herbivore had an opposable finger that, like our thumbs, let it grab and manipulate objects.

Find Out More
on page 29

Pterosaurs

251–65 mya

Pterosaurs, the first vertebrates to evolve powered flight, were not dinosaurs, but they were closely related. All pterosaurs had wings made of a skin membrane stretched between their bodies and the extra-long fourth finger on their hands. Some early pterosaurs had thin, hair-like fibers all over their bodies, which probably helped to keep them warm. (But these fibers weren't actually hair; true hair is found only in mammals!)

Search & find the following pterosaurs.

Pterosaur
(TERR-oh-sore)
Although pterosaurs looked a little like bats, these two groups aren't closely related—pterosaurs were reptiles, and bats are mammals.

Pterosaur Crests
Pterosaurs had elaborate crests on their heads. Some were made of bone, and some were made of keratin (the same thing your hair and fingernails are made of).

Pteranodon
(terr-ANN-oh-don)
Like pelicans and albatrosses today, this large pterosaur probably used rising currents of air to fly around instead of flapping its wings.

Eudimorphodon
(you-di-MORE-foe-don)
Although *Eudimorphodon* was a small pterosaur, it had up to 110 teeth crammed into its tiny 3-inch-long jaws!

Rhamphorynchus
(ram-for-IN-kus)
Rhamphorynchus, like some other early pterosaurs, had a long, stiffened tail that might have helped it change direction rapidly as it flew.

Find Out More on page 30

Marine Reptiles

251–65 mya

While dinosaurs lived on dry land during the Triassic, Jurassic, and Cretaceous Periods, a completely different group of reptiles dominated the world's oceans at that time. Predatory ichthyosaurs, mosasaurs, and plesiosaurs each belonged to reptile groups that returned to the ocean, evolving to survive in a watery environment.

Search & find the following sea creatures.

Ammonite
Although extinct today, these ancient relatives of octopus, squid, and the chambered nautilus were common in Earth's oceans for over 300 million years.

22

Plesiosaur

(PLEASE-ee-oh-sore)

Paleontologists know these reptiles ate ammonites because their crushed shells have been found preserved within plesiosaurs' rib cages.

Sea Turtle

Sea turtles evolved from their land-bound ancestors during the Cretaceous Period, evolving flippers that let them return to the sea.

Flattened Fins

Plesiosaurs used their flattened fins to maneuver through the water and capture their prey.

Mosasaur Teeth

(MOHS-ah-sore)

Mosasaurs had two sets of teeth in their upper jaws; the extra set lined the roof of the mouth!

Ichthyosaur

(ICK-theo-sore)

Ichthyosaurs had the most enormous eyes (compared to their body size) of any animal that has ever lived on Earth.

Squid

Fossil squid sometimes have a preserved ink sac, so ancient squid may have escaped predators by releasing an ink cloud like their modern descendants.

Find Out More on page 30

Fieldwork

Present Day

When paleontologists find a fossil, they don't just start digging up the quarry, which is what paleontologists call a place where they are collecting fossils. Instead, they record as much information as they can about the fossil while it's still in the ground. Paying close attention to the rocks that hold the fossil and how the fossil is laid out can give us clues about what environment the animal lived in, what it ate, and how it moved.

Search & find the following items.

Paleontologist

These scientists study ancient life from fossil remains.

Rock Hammer

Paleontologists use rock hammers to carefully remove layers of rock above the fossil.

Mixing Plaster

Paleontologists carefully encase exposed fossils in plaster casts to protect them on their journey to the laboratory.

Technology

Some paleontologists use ground-penetrating radar to "see" underground before they dig.

Fossils

Fossils are remains or impressions of living things from long ago that have been preserved in the earth and turned into rock.

Grid Drawings

Grids are used to make fossil drawings. The grids help to measure the fossils and their locations, and ensure that drawings are accurate.

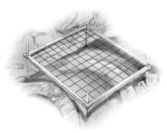

Taking Pictures

As the fossil is gradually dug up, paleontologists take pictures to record its location.

Find Out More
on page 31

24